Richard

Best wishes from

Oct. 20

CW00536194

Fountain of Life

Fountain of Life

music for contemplative worship

Margaret Rizza

Kevin Mayhew

We hope you enjoy the music in this book. Further copies are available
from your local music shop or Christian bookshop.

In case of difficulty, please contact the publisher direct by writing to:

The Sales Department
KEVIN MAYHEW LTD
Buxhall
Stowmarket
Suffolk IP14 3DJ

Phone 01449 737978   Fax 01449 737834

Please ask for our complete catalogue of outstanding Church Music.

Fountain of Life is available as follows:

1400147	**Full score**	includes the complete vocal and instrumental parts
1400148	**Melody edition**	includes melody line, text and guitar chords
1480040	**Cassette**	includes all twelve pieces directed by Margaret Rizza
1490024	**CD**	includes all twelve pieces directed by Margaret Rizza

First published in Great Britain in 1997 by Kevin Mayhew Ltd.

© Copyright 1997 Kevin Mayhew Ltd.

ISBN 1 84003 057 7
ISMN M 57004 134 3
Catalogue No: 1450090

1 2 3 4 5 6 7 8 9

The texts and music in this book are protected by copyright and
may not be reproduced in any way for sale or private use
without the consent of the copyright owner.

Front Cover: *Waterspray*.
Reproduced by courtesy of Images Colour Library Limited, London.
Cover design by Jaquetta Sergeant.

Music Editors: Adrian Vernon Fish and Donald Thomson
Music setting by Donald Thomson
Printed and bound in Great Britain

Contents

Foreword

My heart is ready, O God;
I will play and sing your praise.
Awake, my soul; awake lyre and harp.
I will awake the dawn.
O Lord, I will thank you among the peoples;
I will make music for you among the nations.

from Psalm 108

Fountain of Life was written as a response to a request to compose some music as an introduction to prayer.

Music allows us to enter a world of mystery and imagination. We leave behind our outer external lives which are so bound up with busyness, anxieties, intellectual concerns, plans and projects, to enter into the depths of our inner life. We share and respond to the creative force deep within our being – it is a journey towards 'the centre' to be touched and transformed by beauty and by love.

As we listen, music can perhaps break into our own personal, diverse and conflicting feelings which in turn can resonate with the pain, division and suffering in our world of which we are intrinsically a part. It can also bring us to heights of joy, freedom, gratitude, compassion, worship and praise.

Music can be part of our inner journey which brings us ultimately to the source of love within the ground of our being. It can free us and open up new creative responses which in turn flow out into our everyday life.

So how can music bring us into deeper prayer? In order for our lively minds to become quiet we need music of a meditative, contemplative nature. These very simple chants aim to help still our busy, distracted minds so that we are able to enter into a consciousness of simplicity where all variety, all complexity and multiplicity cease. It is a preparation to enter into the stillness and silence of prayer when we 'leave self behind' (Matthew 16:24-26) to become 'clay in the potter's hand' (Isaiah 64:8).

Each of the twelve pieces in *Fountain of Life* may be sung by one person alone, by two or three gathered together, by hundreds, or by a choir. They may be unaccompanied, accompanied by a single instrument or by a whole music group. They are infinitely expandable according to the resources of those involved. The instrumental variations are graded according to technical skill so there should be something for everyone.

My hope is that the music will be a preparation for prayer, leading to deeper prayer, both for those who sing and play it and for those who listen. I pray that it will bear much fruit.

MARGARET RIZZA

About the composer

Margaret Rizza studied at the Royal College of Music, London, and the National School of Opera, London, and completed her operatic training in Siena and Rome. She has sung at many of the world's leading operatic venues, including La Scala, Milan, Glyndebourne, Sadler's Wells, and with the English Opera Group, and under such conductors as Benjamin Britten, Igor Stravinsky and Leonard Bernstein. She was also a frequent broadcaster.

Since 1977 she has taught singing and voice production at the Guildhall School of Music and Drama in London, and gives master-classes and workshops at summer schools. She also devotes much of her time to helping students to perform and share their music with the marginalised and with people with mental and physical disabilities. In recent years she has worked closely with music therapists.

She has trained and conducted several choirs, and is the founder of The Cameo Opera, The Cameo Singers and the St Thomas Music Group.

Since 1983 she has dedicated herself to the work of spirituality and to the wider aspect of music in the community. She has led many retreats, and is closely involved with the World Community for Christian Meditation (WCCM), as well as leading courses for prayer guides.

Singing these chants

You will find that in using this music most of it can be done very simply indeed by the smallest of groups, singing in unison, or it can be expanded to incorporate much larger forces who have more diverse musical resources at their disposal.

I would like to give some suggestions for both these groups but having said this they are only guidelines and in the end it is you who will decide. Do be adventurous and work on variety. It is lovely to hear the different voices being highlighted, sometimes male, sometimes female, sometimes solo, sometimes children's voices; and then to hear the different colours of the various instruments – all facets of God's life, love and beauty being revealed, poured out and manifested through our musical gifts.

There will naturally be more freedom of choice in the chants which can be as short as 2-3 minutes or as long as 8-10 minutes but even in the other compositions much can be adapted to accommodate the various resources which you have available.

The following Chant Patterns are the ones used for the recording of *Fountain of Life*, but as I have pointed out there are many different ways of working the chants, and in the end it will be your choice.

MAGNIFICAT CHANT PATTERN
1. Introduction: oboe on chant theme with organ.
2. Sopranos on chant theme.
3. Men join unison (or only women). Cello join (basso continuo).
4. Alto variation 1: other voices unison continue on chant.
5. Soprano variation 2: alto variation 1 continue. Other voices continue on chant.
6. Instrumental variation 5: oboe. All voices unison on chant (background).
7. Duet: oboe and recorder. Voices unison on chant (background).
8. Voices SATB. (Unison version: see note at bottom of chant.)
9. Instrumental variations 3 and 4: flute. Voices SATB (background).
10. Instrumental variation 2: violin. Voices SATB (background).

11. Instrumental variation 2: cello. SATB (background).
12. Voices SATB with soprano descant into End bars.
    (N.B. The recording has three more chants.)

For unison voices, where the SATB is introduced at Chant 8 onwards, only the soprano line would be used or if there are altos they could sing their alto line if wanted and it could be used as a two-part version. For the unison version in all the other chants the soprano line will be sung throughout.

YOU ARE THE CENTRE
There is already a pattern indicated with the music which is self-explanatory but for more variety on the first unison singing the women could alternate with the men, each taking four bars up to bar 20. For unison only, the soprano line would be used in the SATB part.

'VENI, LUMEN CORDIUM' CHANT PATTERN
1. Introduction: oboe solo.
2. Sopranos on chant theme with organ, keyboard or guitar.
3. Voices SATB. (Unison version sing soprano line throughout.) Cello join.
4. Instrumental variation 2: oboe. Voices, unison (background).
5. Instrumental variation 3: violin. Voices, unison (background).
6. Voices SATB.
7. Instrumental variation 4: flute. Voices, unison (backgound).
8. Instrumental variation 5: recorder. Voices, unison (background).
9. Voices SATB.
10. Instrumental duet 1: oboe and flute. Voices SATB, hum or ah (background).
11. Instrumental variation 1: cello. Voices SATB, hum or ah (background).
12. Voices SATB plus soprano descant.
13. Last chant. Voices SATB.

COME TO ME
This can be sung either in the SATB version or in a unison version just singing the soprano line.

SEND FORTH YOUR SPIRIT
Introduction: oboe or C instrument or B♭ instrument.
Refrain 1: voices (men and/or women) unison.
Verse 1: solo voice or unison voices.
Refrain 2: men unison (or women). Instrumental refrain variation 2: oboe.
Verse 2: solo voice or unison voices.
Refrain 3: women unison. Instrumental refrain variation 3: flute
Verse 3: solo voice or unison voices.
Last refrain 4: voices SATB (or only women). Instrumental duet 4: flute
or violin and oboe.

ADORAMUS TE, DOMINE DEUS
1. Introductory four bars on organ/keyboard.
2. Soprano on chant theme.
3. Voices SATB. Cello join. (Unison version: sing soprano line throughout.)
4. Instrumental variation 5: oboe. Voices SATB on ah on backing chords.
5. Voices SATB on chant.
6. Instrumental variations 3 and 4: recorder. Voices SATB on ah on backing chords.
7. Instrumental variation 1: flute. Voices SATB on ah on backing chords.
8. Voices SATB on chant.
9. Instrumental variation 2: violin. Voices SATB on ah on backing chords.
10. Voices SATB on chant plus soprano variation.
11. Voices SATB on chant hum. Soprano variation ah.
12. Coda: last chant. Sopranos on words. Others hum.

SILENT, SURRENDERED
1. Introduction. Flute or C instrument on chant theme with organ/keyboard.
2. Sopranos voices on chant themes.
3. Voices SATB. Cello to join. (Unison version: sing soprano line throughout.)

4. Instrumental variation 1: flute. Voices SATB (background).
5. Instrumental variation 2: oboe. Voices SATB (background).
6. Instrumental variation: cello. Voices SATB (background).
7. Instrumental variation 3: violin. Voices SATB (background) with soprano descant 2.
8. Last chant: voices SATB (background) with soprano descant 1.

COME, LORD

This can either be sung in the SATB version as printed or as a unison version following the soprano line. If there are not enough voices to sing the parts in the first 16 introductory bars these can be omitted together with the last six bars of the piece.

JESUS, YOU ARE THE WAY

The soprano or tenor singing the solo verses would need to have some experience in solo singing. However, if a soloist is not available it is quite possible for an instrumentalist (violin, oboe, flute or clarinet, etc.) to take the solo part. In this case the singers would chant the word 'Jesus' and not 'Jesu'. For the unison version the sopranos follow the soprano line throughout.

O LORD, MY HEART IS NOT PROUD

1. Introduction: flute or C instrument on chant theme and organ/ keyboard.
2. Soprano voices on chant theme.
3. Male voices join, unison (or only women's voices). Cello join.
4. Instrumental variation 3: violin. Unison voices (background).
5. Voices SATB. (Unison version: sing or hum soprano line throughout.)
6. Instrumental variation 1: oboe. Voices SATB, hum.
7. Instrumental variation: cello and violin. Voices SATB, hum first 8 bars then sing last 11 bars.

FOUNTAIN OF LIFE

Two versions – for unison singing or SATB – are given and are self-explanatory.

KYRIE, ELEISON

1. Introduction: solo soprano (or C instrument) for the first eight bars.
2. Soprano voices and organ.
3. Voices SATB. Cello joins. (Unison version sing soprano line throughout.)
4. Instrumental variation 1: oboe. Voices SATB on chord backing, hum or ah.
5. Instrumental variation 2: violin. Voices SATB on chord backing, hum or ah.
6. Voices SATB.
7. Instrumental variation 3: flute. Voices SATB on chant.
8. Instrumental variation 4: cello. Voices SATB on chant.
9. Voices SATB.
10. Voices SATB plus soprano descant into Coda bars.

MAGNIFICAT

My soul praises and magnifies the Lord
Text: Luke 1: 46
Music: Margaret Rizza

© Copyright 1997 Kevin Mayhew Ltd.
It is illegal to photocopy music.

YOU ARE THE CENTRE

Text and Music: Margaret Rizza

Pattern Guide

1. Introduction with C instrument to bar 20.
2. Unison voices on theme to bar 20.
3. C instrument variation to bar 20; voices tacet. From bar 21 sing to the end using 2nd time bars.
4. SATB to bar 32 or all sing melody in unison.
5. Instrumental variation; SATB (or unison) hum to bar 20.

© Copyright 1997 Kevin Mayhew Ltd.

It is illegal to photocopy music.

MIXED VOICES

Give me your Spi - rit and teach me your ways, give me your

peace, Lord, and set me free. You are the cen - tre, Lord, of my

life. You are the cen - tre, you are my life,

you are the cen - tre, O Lord, of my life.

VENI, LUMEN CORDIUM

Come, light of our hearts. Come, Holy Spirit, come
Text: Stephen Langton (d.1228); Music: Margaret Rizza

© Copyright 1997 Kevin Mayhew Ltd.
It is illegal to photocopy music.

MIXED VOICES

Ve - ni, lu - men cor - di-um. Ve - ni, San - cte Spi - ri-tus.

Ve - ni, lu - men cor - di-um. Ve - ni, San - cte Spi - ri-tus.

Final Chant

Ve - ni, lu - men cor - di - um.

dim. e rall. al fine

Ve - ni, San - cte Spi - ri - tus. A - men.

dim. e rall. al fine

VOCAL VARIATIONS

Descant 1: Sopranos

Ah, ah.

Descant 2: Sopranos

Ah, ah.

COME TO ME

Text: Matthew 11: 28-30
Music: Margaret Rizza

© Copyright 1997 Kevin Mayhew Ltd.
It is illegal to photocopy music.

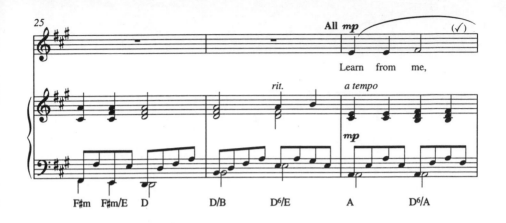

Learn from me, take my yoke. I am meek and gentle, humble of heart.

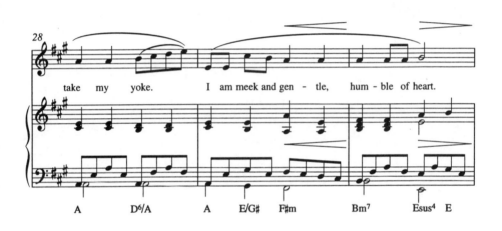

Learn from me, take my yoke. I am meek and gentle,

hum - ble of heart.

rit.   *a tempo*

D/B   D⁶/E   D   E/D Amaj⁷/C#   D/F#   C#/E#

Come   to   me,

A⁷/E   Dmaj⁷ Bm/D   Bm⁷   E⁷sus⁴ E   A   D⁶/A

you   who   thirst;   from   my   heart   liv-ing wa-ters flow.

A   D⁶/A   A   A/G# F#m   Bm⁷   Esus⁴ E

SEND FORTH YOUR SPIRIT

Text: Psalm 104
Music: Margaret Rizza

© Copyright 1997 Kevin Mayhew Ltd.
It is illegal to photocopy music.

21 *D.S al Fine*

clothed in ho-nour and glo-ry, you set the world on its foun-da-tions.
earth is full of your crea-tures, your hand al-ways o-pen to feed them.
sing for e-ver and e-ver, in praise of my God and my King.

D.S al Fine

G   A   D   Em   F♯

MIXED VOICES FOR FINAL REFRAIN

f

S
A

Send forth your Spi-rit, Lord, re-new the face of the earth. Send forth your

T
B

f

f

Dm Dm⁷ Dm Dm/C B♭ Gm/E Asus⁴ A Dm Dm/C

14 *rit.* *Fine*

Spi-rit, Lord, re-new the face of the earth, re-new the face of the earth.

rit. *Fine*

B♭ C F Gm A Dm Gm Dm A⁷ Dm

ADORAMUS TE, DOMINE DEUS

We adore you, O Lord God

Text: Unknown; Music: Margaret Rizza

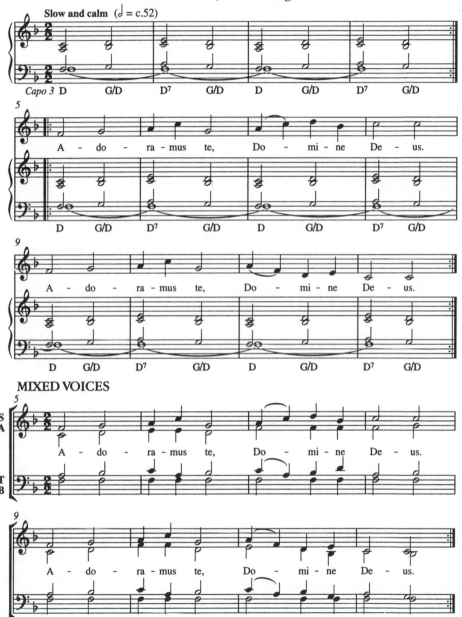

© Copyright 1997 Kevin Mayhew Ltd.
It is illegal to photocopy music.

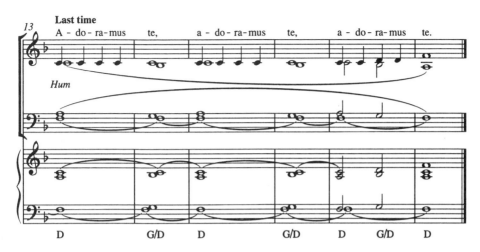

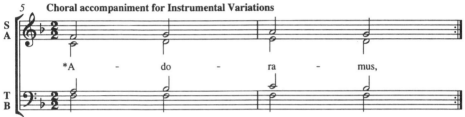

Choral accompaniment for Instrumental Variations

A - do - ra - mus,

* *Or Hum, or 'Ah'*

VOCAL VARIATIONS

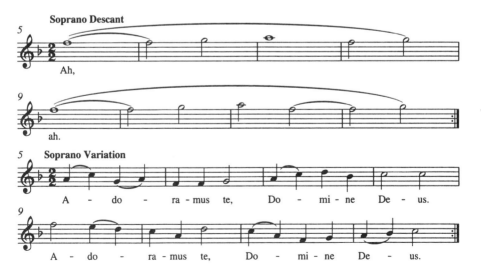

Soprano Descant

Ah,

ah.

Soprano Variation

A - do - ra - mus te, Do - mi - ne De - us.

A - do - ra - mus te, Do - mi - ne De - us.

SILENT, SURRENDERED

Text: v. 1: Pamela Hayes; v. 2: Margaret Rizza
Music: Margaret Rizza

* Additional verse for Pentecost   © Copyright 1997 Kevin Mayhew Ltd.
It is illegal to photocopy music.

VOCAL VARIATIONS

COME, LORD

Text and Music: Margaret Rizza

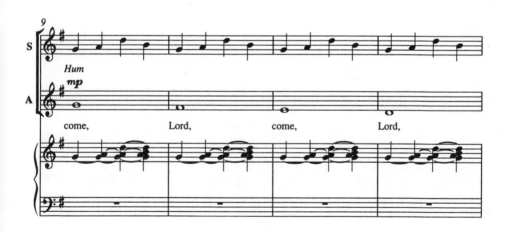

© Copyright 1997 Kevin Mayhew Ltd.
It is illegal to photocopy music.

come to your peo - ple, you are the light in our dark - ness.

Come, Lord, give to us your peace,

Come, Lord, give us peace, come to our war-torn, bro-ken world.

Come, Lord, come, Lord, give us your life, your life e-ter-nal,

JESUS, YOU ARE THE WAY

Text: Pamela Hayes
Music: Margaret Rizza

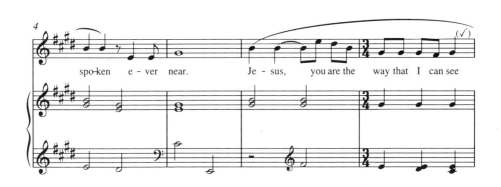

Text © Copyright St Pauls, Morpeth Terrace, London SW1P 1EP. Used by permission.
Music © Copyright 1997 Kevin Mayhew Ltd.
It is illegal to photocopy music.

Je - sus, my wea-ry head has found its rest in the

Je - su, Je - su, Je - su,

beat - ing in your breast. Je - sus, this a - lone can be my prayer,

Je - su, Je - su, Je - su, Je - su,

you are the way, your pierced heart o-pen there.

Je - su, Je - su, Je - su,

Je - sus, you are the way, you are the way.

Je - su, Je - su, Je - su,

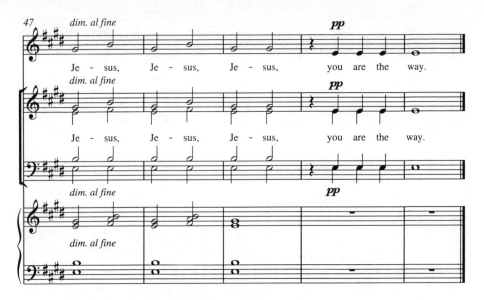

Je - sus, Je - sus, Je - sus, you are the way.

Je - sus, Je - sus, Je - sus, you are the way.

O LORD, MY HEART IS NOT PROUD

Text: Psalm 131
Music: Margaret Rizza

O Lord, my heart is not proud, nor haugh - ty my eyes.

I have not gone af-ter things too great, nor mar - vels be - yond me.

Text from *The Psalms: A New Translation*, translated by The Grail, England.
Used by permission of A.P. Watt Ltd. Music © Copyright 1997 Kevin Mayhew Ltd.
It is illegal to photocopy music.

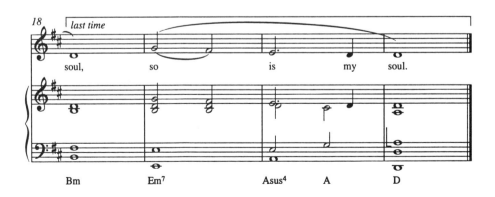

MIXED VOICES

O Lord, my heart is not proud, nor haugh - ty my eyes.

I have not gone af - ter things too great, nor mar - vels be - yond me.

Tru - ly I have set my soul in si - lence and peace; at

rest, as a child in its mo - ther's arms, so is my soul. O

to repeat

last time

soul, so is my soul.

48

Fountain of Life

FOUNTAIN OF LIFE

Text: Michael Forster
Music: Margaret Rizza

UNISON VERSION *(see page 52 for Choral Version)*

© Copyright 1997 Kevin Mayhew Ltd.
It is illegal to photocopy music.

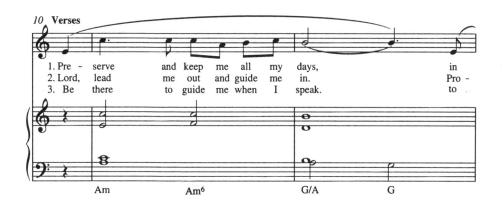

Verses

1. Pre - serve and keep me all my days, in
2. Lord, lead me out and guide me in. Pro -
3. Be there to guide me when I speak. to

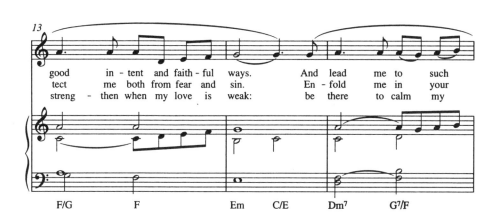

good in - tent and faith - ful ways. And lead me to such
tect me both from fear and sin. En - fold me in your
streng - then when my love is weak: be there to calm my

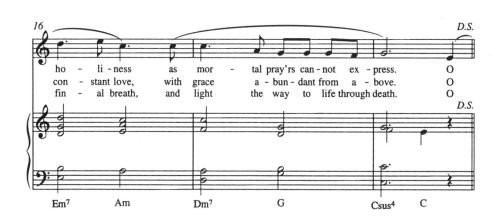

ho - li - ness as mor - tal pray'rs can - not ex - press. O
con - stant love, with grace a - bun - dant from a - bove. O
fin - al breath, and light the way to life through death. O

D.S.

51

CHORAL VERSION *(see page 50 for Unison Version)*

52

there to calm my fi - nal breath, and light the way to life through death. O foun - tain of life, O foun - tain of life, O foun - tain of life, O

Of life, of life,

Of life,

Optional accompaniment

foun - tain of life, O foun - tain of life, O foun - tain of life, O

of life, of life, of life,

foun - tain of life, foun - tain of

55

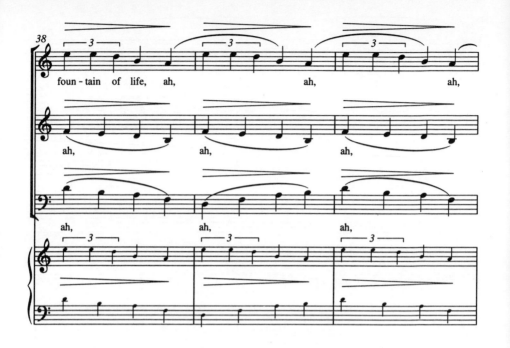

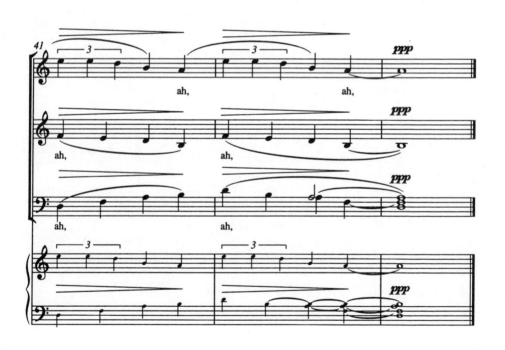

Fountain of Life

KYRIE, ELEISON

Text: Traditional
Music: Margaret Rizza

Lord, have mercy. Christ, have mercy. Lord, hear us.
Christ, have mercy. Lord, have mercy. Christ, hear us.

© Copyright 1997 Kevin Mayhew Ltd.
It is illegal to photocopy music.

MIXED VOICES

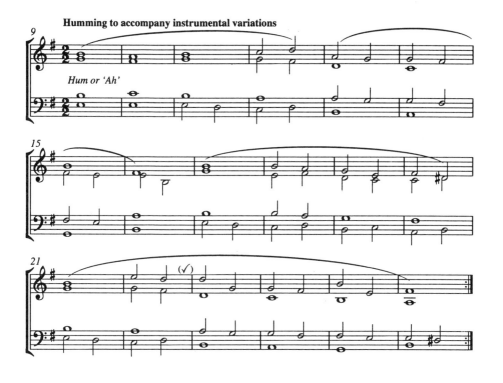

VOCAL VARIATIONS

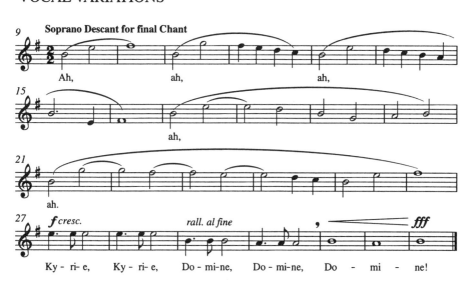